Literature Response Forms

Grades 4-6

Written by Staci Marck
Illustrated by Peggy Collins

ISBN 1-55035-745-X
Copyright 2004
Revised January 2006
All Rights Reserved * Printed in Canada

Published in the United States by:
On the Mark Press
3909 Witmer Road PMB 175
Niagara Falls, New York
14305
www.onthemarkpress.com

Published in Canada by:
S&S Learning Materials
15 Dairy Avenue
Napanee, Ontario
K7R 1M4
www.sslearning.com

At A Glance™

Learning Expectations	Prediction & Inference	Identifying Important Information	Character Analysis	Summarizing Events	Reasoning & Critical Thinking	Vocabulary Development
Understanding Concepts						
• Identify parts of speech - nouns, verbs and adjectives						●
• Identify similes and metaphors, synonyms, prefixes, suffixes, root words		●				
• Use connecting words (first, then, next) to retell a story				●		
• Use a dictionary and thesaurus to expand vocabulary						●
Reading Comprehension						
• Make predictions based on evidence from the text	●	●				
• Identify and describe story elements	●	●	●	●		●
• Identify main idea, provide supporting details		●				
• Summarize story elements, cite supporting evidence	●			●	●	
• Explain how story elements relate to each other			●			
• Retell the story by adapting it for presentation in another way				●		
• Identify and describe character traits, and cite supporting evidence			●			
• Identify and describe similarities and differences	●		●			
• Identify cause and effect relationships		●		●	●	
• Make connections between the story and personal experiences/the real world	●	●	●	●	●	
• Make inferences based on personal interpretation of the story	●	●	●	●	●	
• Make judgements and draw conclusions using evidence from the story	●	●	●	●	●	
• Develop opinions and express personal point of view		●	●	●	●	
• Identify the point of view of the author or a character	●			●		
• Distinguish between fact and fiction using evidence from the text		●				
• Create a media text - advertisement					●	
• Creative writing - sequel to the story, join the story, rewrite the ending	●				●	
• Forms of writing - book review, book report, biography, letter to a character		●			●	●
• Express own interpretation of a story through visual and performing arts (illustrations, picture book, theatrical script, book cover)			●	●	●	

Literature Response Forms

Table of Contents

Teacher Assessment Rubric

Student's Name: _____

Put a check mark in the box that indicates the student's level of achievement.

Level 1 - requires assistance, inconsistent effort, shows limited understanding of concepts
Level 2 - requires minimal assistance, shows limited understanding of concepts
Level 3 - independent, consistent effort, shows general understanding of concepts
Level 4 - independent, consistent effort, shows thorough understanding of concepts

Criteria	Level 1	Level 2	Level 3	Level 4
Prediction and Inference				
• Uses knowledge and experience to make predictions.				
• Uses evidence from the text to make inferences and support predictions.				
Identifying Important Information				
• Identifies main idea and provides supporting details.				
• Evaluates story elements and conclusion/resolution				
• Draws conclusions and makes generalizations based on his/her personal interpretation of the story.				
Character Analysis				
• Demonstrates an understanding of character traits.				
• Uses knowledge of character to evaluate roles, and cites supporting details from the text.				
Summarizing Events				
• Retells a story in proper sequence with supporting details.				
• Identifies and describes story elements.				
Reasoning and Critical Thinking				
• Makes connections between the story and the real world.				
• Makes judgements and draws conclusions about the text's content using supporting evidence.				
Vocabulary Development				
• Understands the text at a word level.				
• Uses knowledge of language structures and word categories.				
• Uses a dictionary and thesaurus to expand vocabulary.				

Comments: _____

_____

_____

Student Self-Assessment Rubric

Name: _____ Date: _____

Put a check mark in the box that best describes your performance, then add your points to determine your total score.

Expectations	Actual Performance (measured in points)				
	1 - Needs Improvement	2 - Sometimes	3 - Frequently	4 - Always/almost always	Points
✔ I remained focused and on task.					
✔ I was prepared and organized.					
✔ I used all the resources available.					
✔ I reread parts of the book so I could adjust off-target predictions.					
✔ I used my own experiences and knowledge to support predictions.					
✔ I used my text to support ideas.					
✔ I edited and proofread my work.					
✔ I know what I am good at.					
✔ I know what I need to work on.					

Total Points: _____

Questions for personal reflection:

1. What did you find most interesting, and enjoy learning about the most?

2. What questions do you still have, and what would you like to learn more about?

3. What can you improve upon, and how can you make this improvement?

4. What is your overall impression of your work?

Literature Response Forms

Planning and Implementation Guide

1. **Why Use Literature Response Forms?**

   • Reading comprehension is the process in which a reader builds meaning from a text and his or her prior knowledge. It involves thinking before, during, and after the reading process. Assessment of reading comprehension can only be done indirectly because it is a thought process.

   • Literature response forms help you assess your students' understanding of the texts they are reading. The activities in this resource encourage students to make creative connections between the text and their previous learning, thereby strengthening their comprehension.

   • Literature response forms are engaging, meaningful activities that students can complete on their own during Reader's Workshop. This opens up classroom time for you to conduct guided reading lessons in small groups, or to conference with individual students.

   • These work sheets provide authentic assessment information on student skill levels. The analysis of completed activities will help you determine the next steps in planning and programing to meet individual student needs.

2. **Introducing Literature Response Forms in a Mini-Lesson**

   • Literature response forms should be introduced in a whole class mini-lesson after a shared reading. Choose a book that supports the skill focus of the work sheet that you wish to introduce.

   • Explicitly teach your students the skill focus of the response form using an enlarged copy of the work sheet on an overhead, the chalkboard, or chart paper, so that all of the students can easily see the template. Explain the concepts being introduced. Use a "think aloud" strategy to model your thinking as you complete the form, so that the students can see the process you go through to respond. Engage the students in a guided practice process by asking them questions, encouraging discussion, and recording a variety of their responses which highlight the range of possibilities of appropriate responses.

   • After the mini-lesson, have the students practice completing the work sheet as a response to an independent reading of their own text selections.

   • Use this mini-lesson format to introduce each new literature response form.

   • Once several response forms have been explicitly taught and modeled, and the students have had sufficient practice working with them, they can be used as independent literature responses for shared, guided, or independent reading comprehension assessment.

   • Introduce literature response forms based on the individual and collective learning needs of your students. You may wish to introduce work sheets from all six skill areas so that students can develop a range of skills at varying levels of difficulty.

Literature Response Forms

3. **Organizing Literature Response Forms**

   - Literature response forms can be organized in a variety of different ways. Students can be given a package of literature response forms to complete within a specified time frame during Reader's Workshop. For example, you may allot two weeks, or approximately ten sessions, for students to complete six to ten different work sheets.

   - Alternatively, individual response forms may be kept in bins, and students may be given free choice to select the response form that best suits their text selection. Ensure that they understand how many responses they are required to complete, and how much time during Reader's Workshop they have to complete them.

   - You may also wish to assign specific response forms to individual students who require additional practice in one or more skill areas.

   - The response forms can also be used as literature circle roles within novel study groups. Each member of the group should be assigned a different response to complete once they have read a particular section of the novel. Each member then shares his/her response with the rest of the reading group.

   - Alternate the response forms that are available for students to select so that they can develop, practice and master a variety of skills. Varying literature response activities will also ensure that students' motivation remains constant.

4. **Sharing Responses**

   - Allow time for students to share their responses so that they may celebrate their accomplishments. Sharing helps to develop a community of motivated learners who gather new ideas from peers, and recommend reading materials to one another. Sharing also helps to foster self-confidence in individual students as they discuss their responses.

   - Sharing can be done weekly, as a whole class, or through individual assignments to a group or the class on particular days. It can also be done daily, within guided reading groups during assigned sharing time, at the end of the reading session.

5. **Helping Students Select Appropriate Reading Texts**

   - **Shared reading** or **read aloud** texts can be at any reading level because the teacher is reading the text and modeling the process to the students.

   - **Guided reading** texts should be chosen so that students within the group can read it with 90 to 94 percent accuracy and comprehension. The text is slightly harder than that which they can read independently because they will receive scaffolded teacher support during the lesson.

   - **Independent reading** or **novel study** texts should be at the student's "just right" level - a book that the student can read on his/her own at greater than 95 percent accuracy. If the student makes more than five reading errors on the first page, then the text is too difficult.

Literature Response Forms

6. **Tracking, Assessment and Individual Programing**

   • The **Personal Reading Record** (p. 15) and **Literature Response Tracking Sheet** (p. 16) are to be completed by each student independently, and are useful tools for monitoring independent reading activity and skill area completion.

   • A collection of a student's completed litereature response forms provides an extensive overview of his/her reading comprehension skills. In addition, **teacher-student conferences** may be conducted to gather performance-based assessment information and direct individual programing. You may follow the format on the conference form provided (p. 13) to bring meaningful structure to these sessions.

   • The **assessment rubrics** (p. 4 and 5) are useful aides for gathering information on a student's strengths and needs, and should be used to direct independent instruction and mini-lessons. They will also provide feedback to students on their progress and guide them in setting personal learning goals.

7. **Using the Blank Forms**

   • Blank forms are included in this resource (p. 77) that can be used to create additional activities in order to meet individual student needs, and the needs of the classroom.

Modeling the Literature Response Activities

In this section you will find suggestions for modeling the six different types of response forms in your mini-lessons. One example is given for each of the skill categories. The first one, using the Predict-Read-Check work sheet as an example for the prediction and inference activities, is described in detail from start to finish of the mini-lesson. You may adapt this modeling format, as needed, to introduce any of the literature response forms in this resource. Be sure to read "Introducing Literature Response Forms in a Mini-Lesson" (p. 6) prior to reading the modeling suggestions below.

Keep in mind as you plan your mini-lessons, that there are a variety of possible approaches and timings for the completion of many of the forms. Choose from among these options the approach that best suits the unique needs of your students. The variations are noted in the sections below.

Prediction and Inference:

Research shows that effective readers preview the text, set a purpose for reading, make predictions, reflect on what they have learned, and draw conclusions from the text. Prediction and inference are two essential components of comprehension employed at the first stage of reading. Being able to predict and infer prepares students for reading a text and understanding it.

The prediction and inference activities challenge students to draw on their prior knowledge about a topic before reading the text, and make connections between this knowledge and what they learn as they read. By making predictions before reading, and then checking their predictions after reading, students have the opportunity to discover how much they already know about the topic.

Literature Response Forms

Activity Variations:

- Many of these activities may be expanded by having students provide additional information on the back of the work sheet, such as details from the story verifying the accuracy of their predictions, and other kinds of supporting evidence for their answers.

Example: Predict-Read-Check (p. 17)

- Begin the mini-lesson by showing the students the book cover, telling them the title, and reading the synopsis on the back cover of the book. Ask the students to make predictions about what they think they will learn, following the outline of the response form.

- Record their responses on the enlarged copy of the form that you have displayed at the front of the class.

- Tell the students to think about what the author is trying to say as they listen to the story. Then, read the section of the book and record the page numbers.

- When you are finished reading the section, ask the students to tell you what they think the author is trying to say in this section. Record a few of their thoughts.

- For the next the question, use a "Think-Pair-Share" activity. Ask the students to write down two questions they had while reading this section, or that they still have from a previous section of the book. Have the students share their thoughts with a partner for a minute or two. Record a few of the questions from students who wish to share with the class as part of the model.

- Repeat the Think-Pair-Share exercise, this time focusing on what they have learned so far from the reading. Ask a few students to share their summaries with the entire class, and record their responses for the class to analyze. Discuss to what extent, and how, they are on the right track, and what important details, if any, are missing. Explicitly show the students the kind of summary you expect to receive.

- Finally, as a class, reflect on how the text matched or did not match the original predictions.

- Provide each student with their own copy of the literature response form that you have just modeled, and let them practice completing it with their own text selections. Check for understanding and mastery before giving it to students to complete during Reader's Workshop.

Identifying Important Information

In this section, students learn to distinguish between important and extraneous information, and identify main ideas. Students will also learn about specific language structures used in their texts, such as similes and metaphors.

Activity Variations:

- For work sheets that do not already require supporting evidence, students may provide such evidence for their answers on the back of the page.

Literature Response Forms

Example: Analytical Analyzer (p. 30)

- Begin the mini-lesson by telling the students that they will be learning to identify important information in the story, and reflecting on what it means to each of them by relating it to their personal experiences.

- Ask the students to listen for things that they find interesting in the story as you read it aloud. These might include exact phrases from the book or general ideas relating to things the characters say, events that unfold, descriptions of characters or the setting, etc.

- Begin reading, and stop part way through the section to record students' comments under the heading, "Details from the Book".

- When you are finished reading the section, and have recorded a variety of students' responses in the first column, have them do a Think-Pair-Share activity, focusing on their thoughts and feelings about one of the items listed in the first column. Ask a few students to share with the class, and record their responses under the heading, "Analysis". You may wish to describe and record your own responses to demonstrate exactly the sort of response you are looking for.

Character Analysis

These work sheets focus the students' attention on the characters in the book, what they are like, how they live, and the ways they solve problems. Readers are challenged to identify similarities and differences between themselves and the characters, and between the characters and people they know. Characters are frequently the most memorable part of a story to children. Analyzing the behaviors of these characters helps bring them to life, and engages students in such thought provoking questions as "What would this character be like if he or she lived in my city, or even next door?"

Activity Variations:

- These work sheets may be completed while the text is being read or after the text has been finished. For an added challenge, have students provide supporting evidence for their answers on the back of the work sheet. Although meant to be individual activities, these literature response forms are excellent discussion starters to share in reading groups.

Example: Character Web (p. 37)

- Start the mini-lesson by telling the students that they will be analyzing a text to identify character traits of the main character. Define character traits as the ways a character behaves, looks, thinks, feels and responds to others in the story.

- Introduce the book and identify the main character that you will be analyzing. Ask the students to think about his or her character traits as you read the selection.

- Begin reading, and stop midway through the section to check for understanding. Have the students do a Think-Pair-Share activity, focusing on the traits they have heard about so far. Record a few responses on the form before continuing the reading.

Literature Response Forms

- Repeat the same procedure when you have finished reading the section. Record a few of the students' examples, and ask them to confirm whether or not the responses are character traits based on the definition you provided.

Summarizing Events

These work sheets focus on reviewing the elements of a story. Story elements include the setting, characters, problem, events, and solution/resolution of the story. The 5W questions (Who, What, Where, When, and Why) are often used in conjunction with How to prompt the retell of the story. Readers are challenged to retell the story in the sequence it occurred in the book. Each story element is a crucial component to the story, so every element must be remembered during the retell on the response activity.

Activity Variations:

- Same as for the Character Analysis work sheets (see p. 10).

Example: First, Then, Next (p. 48)

- Tell the students that they will be learning how to retell a story using story elements. Define story elements as the setting, characters, problem, events, and solution/resolution of the story.

- Introduce the book and identify the subject, genre, or chapter to be summarized. Remind the students to focus on identifying the story elements as you read.

- Begin reading, and stop midway through the section to check for understanding. Have the students do a Think-Pair-Share activity, focusing on one story element they have heard described so far. Record a few responses on the form before continuing the reading.

- Repeat the same procedure once you have finished reading the section. Record a few of the students' examples for the remaining questions on the form. Then ask them to confirm whether or not their responses are story elements based on the definition you provided.

Reasoning and Critical Thinking

These exercises require students to evaluate and modify the text using their own ideas, experiences and imagination. Readers are challenged to bring new life to the story by adding new characters, joining the story, and changing the ending, etc. By applying their knowledge of the story in these ways, they have opportunities to develop an advanced level of comprehension and demonstrate higher order thinking skills.

Activity Variations:

- A few of these work sheets may be completed during reading, however most are to be completed after the entire text has been read. Sharing student responses in small reading groups or with the whole class creates opportunities for thought provoking discussions, stimulating the students' creativity.

Literature Response Forms

Example: Biography (p. 57)

- Start the mini-lesson by telling the students that, as a group, they will be learning how to write a biography about a character from a story. Define biography as a written account of a person's life that presents real events from the life of the subject. The events an author chooses to include help readers understand why the person is important, and how he or she thinks, feels, and behaves in the setting in which the person lives.

- Introduce the book and identify the character to be studied. Tell the students to listen as you read for interesting facts about the character that will help someone who is not familiar with the person come to know and understand him or her.

- Begin reading the text, and stop midway through the section to check for understanding. Have the students do a Think-Pair-Share activity, focusing on one interesting fact they have heard so far. Record a few of the students' responses on the chalkboard and label them, "Interesting facts about _____". Then continue the reading.

- Repeat the same procedure once you have finished reading the section. Add a few more examples from students to the list. Then ask them to confirm if these facts are interesting and informative enough to be included in a biography.

Vocabulary Development

These work sheets focus on the analysis of language conventions used in the story. As students build their understanding of vocabulary and language structures, they develop a deeper understanding of the story itself.

Activity Variations

- Students may complete these forms while the text is being read or after they have finished reading it. They may expand on their answers by providing supporting evidence on the back of the work sheet.

Example: Is It Really a Noun? (p. 67)

- At the start of the mini-lesson, give the students the definition of a noun (a person, animal, place or thing).

- While reading the book, have students listen for nouns that they hear in the story.

- Midway through the section, stop reading and have the students do a Think-Pair-Share activity, focusing on one noun they have heard so far. Record a few of the students' responses on the chalkboard before continuing the reading. Repeat the same procedure once you have finished reading the section.

- Then, using the response form template, ask the students to identify a sentence from the text that they would like to examine. Write the sentence on the template, and have the students identify the noun in that sentence. Ask them to explain why they think this word is a noun. By explaining their reasoning, the exercise becomes more meaningful, and they are more likely to remember what a noun is. Have another student verify that the word is indeed a noun by looking it up in the dictionary. Repeat this process to complete the form.

Teacher-Student Conference Form

Student's Name: _____ **Date:** _____

Title: _____ **Chapter:** _____

Record of Student's Retelling:

- Identifies setting, time and place.   Yes ☐   No ☐
- Names main character.   Yes ☐   No ☐
- States main character's problem.   Yes ☐   No ☐
- Mentions other characters.   Yes ☐   No ☐
- Uses story vocabulary in the retelling.   Yes ☐   No ☐

- Identifies main idea and provides supporting details.   Yes ☐   No ☐
  Comments: _____
  _____

- Provides plot details in sequential order.   Yes ☐   No ☐
  Comments: _____
  _____

- Makes inferences.   Yes ☐   No ☐
  Comments: _____
  _____

- Makes connections with the text.   Yes ☐   No ☐
  Comments: _____
  _____

Additional Comments: _____
_____
_____

Literature Response Forms

List of Work Sheets

Prediction and Inference
1. Predict-Read-Check
2. Reading Preparation
3. Questioning the Author
4. Events and Emotions
5. Before and After
6. Text-to-Me
7. Make a Connection
8. Sequel
9. What I Think I Know
10. Story Study Predictions

Character Analysis
1. Character Web
2. Real Life versus Fiction
3. Character Impressions
4. Your Traits - My Traits
5. Portrait Gallery
6. Character Scrutiny
7. Character Evaluation
8. Sketch Artist
9. Feelings
10. Character Attribute Web

Reasoning and Critical Thinking
1. Biography
2. Add a New Character
3. Creative Designer
4. Join the Story
5. The Finale
6. Write a Letter
7. Text-to-Text Connections
8. How Would You Solve It?
9. Novel Conflict
10. Cover Illustrator

Identifying Important Information
1. Book Critic
2. Getting the Main Idea
3. Chain of Events
4. Analytical Analyzer
5. Chapter Chatter
6. Problem Solver
7. Reaching the Peak
8. Fact or Fiction?
9. Comparisons: Similes/Metaphors
10. Guess-Check-Prove It!

Summarizing Events
1. Star Story Plotter
2. First, Then, Next
3. Story Stones
4. Story Path
5. Story Steps
6. Playwright
7. Basic Book Report
8. Event Story Map
9. Nonfiction Retell Outline
10. 5W Story Map

Vocabulary Development
1. Is It Really a Noun?
2. Abstract Nouns
3. The Clothes Nouns Wear
4. Vocabulary Expansion
5. Picturing Adjectives
6. Get a Clue!
7. Voracious Verbs
8. Add-Ons
9. End-Its
10. Triangular Account

Personal Reading Record

_____'s Reading Record

Date	Title	Author	Genre	#Pages

Genre Key: F - Fiction   NF - Nonfiction   P - Poetry

Literature Response Tracking Sheet

Name: _____

Color the box of each completed activity.

Prediction and Inference

- ☐ 1. Predict-Read-Check
- ☐ 2. Reading Preparation
- ☐ 3. Questioning the Author
- ☐ 4. Events and Emotions
- ☐ 5. Before and After
- ☐ 6. Text-to-Me
- ☐ 7. Make a Connection
- ☐ 8. Sequel
- ☐ 9. What I Think I Know
- ☐ 10. Story Study Predictions

Identifying Important Information

- ☐ 1. Book Critic
- ☐ 2. Getting the Main Idea
- ☐ 3. Chain of Events
- ☐ 4. Analytical Analyzer
- ☐ 5. Chapter Chatter
- ☐ 6. Problem Solver
- ☐ 7. Reaching the Peak
- ☐ 8. Fact or Fiction?
- ☐ 9. Comparisons
- ☐ 10. Guess-Check-Prove It!

Character Analysis

- ☐ 1. Character Web
- ☐ 2. Real Life versus Fiction
- ☐ 3. Character Impressions
- ☐ 4. Your Traits - My Traits
- ☐ 5. Portrait Gallery
- ☐ 6. Character Scrutiny
- ☐ 7. Character Evaluation
- ☐ 8. Sketch Artist
- ☐ 9. Feelings
- ☐ 10. Character Attribute Web

Summarizing Events

- ☐ 1. Star Story Plotter
- ☐ 2. First, Then, Next
- ☐ 3. Story Stones
- ☐ 4. Story Path
- ☐ 5. Story Steps
- ☐ 6. Playwright
- ☐ 7. Basic Book Report
- ☐ 8. Event Story Map
- ☐ 9. Nonfiction Retell
- ☐ 10. 5W Story Map

Reasoning and Critical Thinking

- ☐ 1. Biography
- ☐ 2. Add a New Character
- ☐ 3. Creative Designer
- ☐ 4. Join the Story
- ☐ 5. The Finale
- ☐ 6. Write a Letter
- ☐ 7. Text-to-Text Connections
- ☐ 8. How Would You Solve It?
- ☐ 9. Novel Conflict
- ☐ 10. Cover Illustrator

Vocabulary Development

- ☐ 1. Is It Really a Noun?
- ☐ 2. Abstract Nouns
- ☐ 3. Clothes Nouns Wear
- ☐ 4. Vocabulary Expansion
- ☐ 5. Picturing Adjectives
- ☐ 6. Get a Clue!
- ☐ 7. Voracious Verbs
- ☐ 8. Add-Ons
- ☐ 9. End-Its
- ☐ 10. Triangular Account

Predict-Read-Check

Before reading a new section of the text, **complete the prediction** box of the outline. As you read, complete the other boxes.

Predict what you think you will learn.
_____
_____
_____
_____

Read the section. Note the page numbers read.
_____
_____
_____

Think about what the author is saying.
_____
_____
_____
_____

Questions I have about _____

1. _____
   _____

2. _____
   _____

Prediction Confirmation (Am I on the right track?)
_____
_____
_____

Summary of things I've learned thus far: _____
_____
_____
_____
_____
_____

Prediction and Inference #1

Name: _____

Date: _____

Title: _____

Author: _____

Reading Preparation

Prepare for reading your book by answering the following questions.

1. When was this book written?

   _____

   _____

2. Who is the publisher of the book?

   _____

   _____

3. How many pages are in the book?

   _____

   _____

4. What does the title suggest to you about the book?

   _____

   _____

5. What do you predict the book will be about, based on the cover?

   _____

   _____

6. Read three pages of the book – one from the beginning, one from the middle, and one near the end of the book. What do you predict about the book from these pages?

   _____

   _____

   _____

   _____

Prediction and Inference #2

Name: _____
Date: _____
Title: _____
Author: _____

Questioning the Author

Select a chapter from the **middle** of the book to answer the following questions.

1. What is the author's message in this chapter?

   _____
   _____
   _____
   _____

2. How do you know this is what the author was trying to say?

   _____
   _____
   _____
   _____

3. How does this new information connect with what the author has said in previous chapters?

   _____
   _____
   _____
   _____

4. What do you predict will happen next in the story? Why?

   _____
   _____
   _____
   _____

Prediction and Inference #3

Name: _____
Date: _____
Title: _____
Author: _____

Events and Emotions Inference Chart

Fill in the boxes in the flow chart with the **events** portrayed in the story in **sequential order**. In the ovals beneath the boxes, state what **emotion** or feeling is inferred by the main character due to the event.

Example:

Karana's befriending of the leader of the wild dogs in Island of the Blue Dolphins.

Love

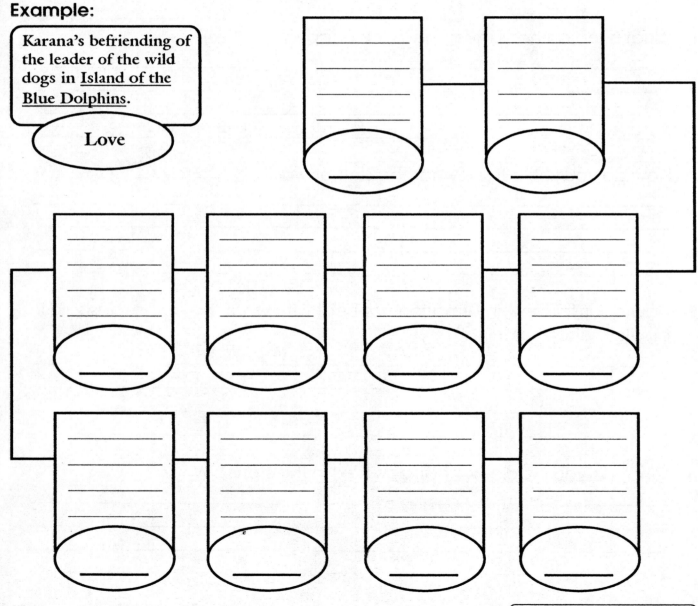

Prediction and Inference #4

Name: _____
Date: _____
Title: _____
Author: _____

Before and After

Before reading each chapter, complete the first column of the chart. Note what you predict or **hope to learn** from the chapter.

After reading the chapter, note **what you actually learned** from the chapter in the second column.

What I hope to learn from:	What I actually learned:
Chapter __:	
Chapter __:	
Chapter __:	
Chapter __:	
Chapter __:	
Chapter __:	
Chapter __:	

Prediction and Inference #5

Text-to-Me

In each section below, **compare** your world to the main character's world in your novel. How are they similar? How do they differ?

_____ 's World

_____
_____
_____

My World

_____
_____
_____
_____

_____ 's World

_____
_____
_____

My World

_____
_____
_____
_____

_____ 's World

_____
_____
_____

My World

_____
_____
_____

_____ 's World

_____
_____
_____

My World

_____
_____
_____

Prediction and Inference #6

Make a Connection

There are three main connections that can be made with a text: **Text-to-Text**, **Text-to-Me**, and **Text-to-World**. Show your personal connections by sharing your thoughts below.

1. What did you think the book was going to be about before reading it?

   _____
   _____
   _____

2. Compare this book to another that you have read. How are they similar?

   _____
   _____
   _____

3. What event in your life does the story make you think of?

   _____
   _____
   _____

4. What world happening does the story remind you of?

   _____
   _____
   _____

5. Was your original prediction about the book valid? Why or why not?

   _____
   _____
   _____

Prediction and Inference #7

Name: _____
Date: _____
Title: _____
Author: _____

Sequel

In your own words, **summarize** what happened at the end of the story. Then, write a short **sequel** to the story that continues where the story left off.

Remember the **5W's** when writing your paragraph:

- **Who** did something?
- **What** did they do or say?
- **How** did they do them?
- **Where** did they go?
- **Why** did they do these things?

At the end of the story _____
_____
_____
_____

The sequel begins when_____
_____
_____
_____
_____
_____
_____
_____
_____
_____
_____
_____

Prediction and Inference #8

Name: _____
Date: _____
Title: _____
Author: _____

What I Think I Know

Before Reading:

- Think about your book's title and cover illustration. In the first column, record what you think you already know about this subject.

- Think about what you would like to learn about this subject, and record your thoughts in the second column.

After Reading:

- Record what you learned and what you still wonder about in the last two columns.

What I **Think** I Know	What I **Want** to Know	What I **Learned**	What I Still **Wonder** About

Story Study Predictions

- **Before** you read your book, look at the front and back covers, and the title. Thumb through the pages.
- Ask yourself the 5W's and How. **Predict Who**, **What**, **Where**, **When**, **Why** and **How** the story will unfold. Write your predictions below.
- **After** reading, check your predictions. On the back of this page, note how your predictions compared to the real story.

1. Who will be in the story?

   _____

   _____

2. When will the story take place?

   _____

   _____

3. Where will the story take place?

   _____

   _____

4. What do you think will happen?

   _____

   _____

5. What will the overall theme be?

   _____

   _____

6. How will the events unfold?

   _____

   _____

7. Why do you think these things will happen?

   _____

   _____

Prediction and Inference #10

Name: _____
Date: _____
Title: _____
Author: _____

Book Critic

You are a book reviewer for a magazine. Your job is to report the facts about a story. Should others read this story? Why or why not? **Who** is the story about? **Where** does it take place? **When** does it take place? **What** happens in the story? **Why** and **how** do these events happen? Answer these questions to write a persuasive article that critically analyzes the book. Remember to include a catchy title that grabs the reader's attention, such as, "Sequatchie Sighting, Big Feet or Big Foot?"

_____

Reported by _____

_____
_____
_____
_____
_____
_____
_____
_____
_____
_____
_____
_____
_____
_____
_____

Identifying Important Information #1

Getting the Main Idea

Identify the main idea of the text, and provide supporting details to clarify your answer.

Main Idea
_____
_____
_____
_____
_____

Supporting Detail 1
_____
_____
_____
_____

Supporting Detail 2
_____
_____
_____
_____

Supporting Detail 3
_____
_____
_____
_____

Identifying Important Information #2

Name: _____
Date: _____
Title: _____
Author: _____

Chain of Events

Each action or event in a text is affected by the event that precedes it. This cause-and-effect relationship is like a chain of events.

Show the chain of events in the text. List the first action or event that occurs in the first box.

List each subsequent event in the order in which they occur.

Cause-and-Effect Chain for _____

Identifying Important Information #3

Name: _____

Date: _____

Title: _____

Author: _____

Analytical Analyzer

- What things did you find especially interesting as you read this book? Identify **1)** things the characters said or did, **2)** descriptions of the characters, setting, or events, and **3)** other interesting details. List them in the first column.

- Analyze each item in the first column by recording what you think or feel about them in the second column. Why is it interesting to you? What does it make you think of? Who or what does it remind you of? How does it make you feel?

Details from the Book...	My Analysis...

Identifying Important Information #4

Name: _____

Date: _____

Title: _____

Author: _____

Chapter Chatter

Summarize your book or chapter by completing the graphic organizer.

Think about what the author was telling you with reference to: the **main character**, his or her **goal**, the **problem** that interferes with achieving this goal, and the solution to the problem (how was the goal achieved?).

Main Character	**His or her goal**

The problem	**The solution to the problem**

Identifying Important Information #5

Problem Solver

Identify the plot or problem in the book and how it was resolved by completing the organizer.

Problem
_____
_____
_____
_____

First Event
_____
_____
_____
_____

Second Event
_____
_____
_____
_____

Third Event
_____
_____
_____
_____

Resolution
_____
_____
_____
_____

Identifying Important Information #6

Name: _____
Date: _____
Title: _____
Author: _____

Reaching the Peak

The **climax** is the **highest point of conflict**, or the turning point before the problem is resolved in the story. Identify **three events** that led up to the climax, and record them in the triangle.

Events leading up to the climax:

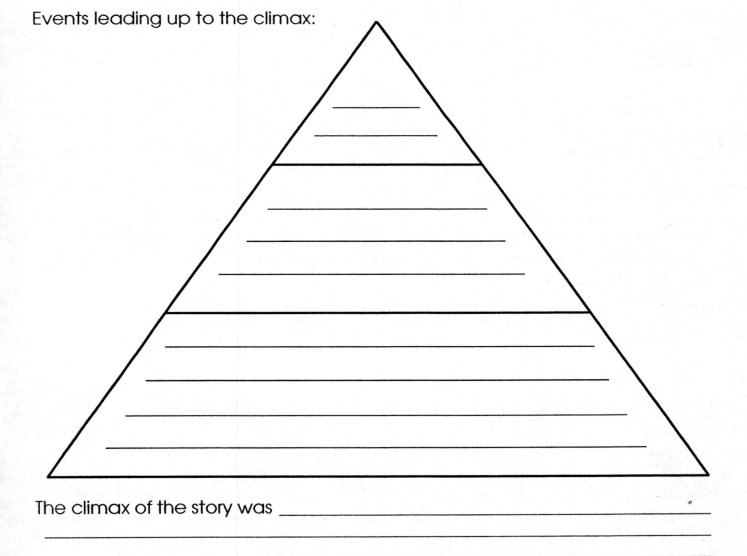

The climax of the story was _____
_____
_____

Name: _____

Date: _____

Title: _____

Author: _____

Fact or Fiction?

Books are either **fiction** (made up) or **nonfiction** (true or factual). List the reasons why you think the book is fiction or nonfiction. Give **specific examples** from your book, and list the **page number** where you found the information.

This book is ☐ fiction ☐ nonfiction because:

1. _____
   _____

   Page _____

2. _____
   _____

   Page _____

3. _____
   _____

   Page _____

4. _____
   _____

   Page _____

5. _____
   _____

   Page _____

6. _____
   _____

   Page _____

Identifying Important Information #8

Name: _____

Date: _____

Title: _____

Author: _____

Comparisons: Similes and Metaphors

Writers relay complex ideas to the reader by using **similes** and **metaphors**. A **simile** compares two unlike things and always begins with the words *like* or *as*. For example, "Life is like a box of chocolates" from the movie <u>Forest Gump</u>.

A **metaphor** emphasizes the similarities between two different things or ideas without using any identifier words such as *like* or *as*. For example, the librarian who helps Bud says, "… knowledge is a food" (<u>Bud, Not Buddy</u>, p. 91). Find **one simile** and **one metaphor** in the story and copy each one in the appropriate spaces. Note the **page number** where you found them. **Explain** what ideas you think the author is comparing.

Page ____ **Simile**: _____

_____

_____

I think the author is comparing _____

_____

_____

Page ____ **Metaphor**: _____

_____

_____

I think the author is comparing _____

_____

_____

Identifying Important Information #9

Name: _____
Date: _____
Title: _____
Author: _____

Guess-Check-Prove It!

Before reading the text, look at the title, cover illustration, flip through the pages, and read the synopsis on the back cover.

What do you think the book will be about? What makes you think this?

- Using the **5W's** (Who? What? Where? When? Why?) **predict** five questions that you think the author will address in the story.
- **Read** the book and look for proof that confirms your predictions.
- **Record** the proof from the story and the page number it is on.

Predictions	Proof	Page
Who		
What		
Where		
When		
Why		

Identifying Important Information # 10

Name: _____

Date: _____

Title: _____

Author: _____

Character Web

In the web, list **five character traits** of the main character in your story. What is he or she like? How does he or she act? How does he or she feel? Include the **page number** where the character trait was seen in the story.

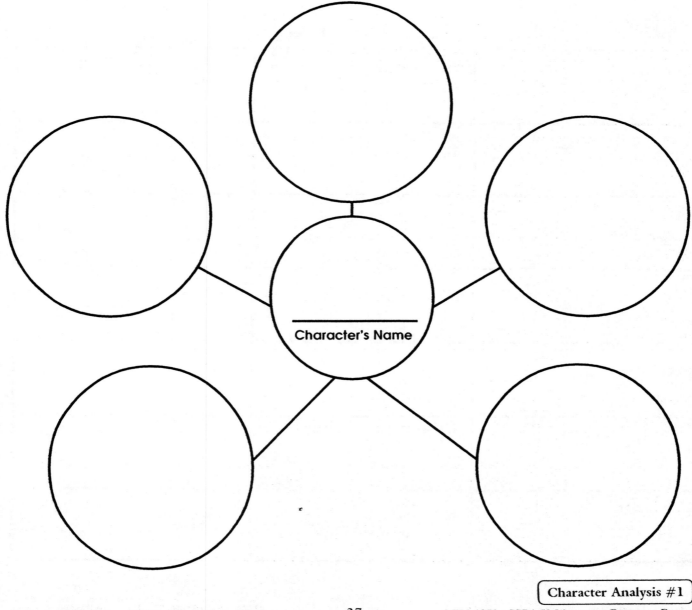

Character's Name

Character Analysis #1

Name: _____
Date: _____
Title: _____
Author: _____

Real Life versus Fiction

How are fictional characters' lives different from real life? In the chart below, write out features of your life and features of the main character's life from your novel. In the middle column, list the features that are the same in both your life and the character's life.

Complete the chart.

My life...	Both our lives...	_____'s life...

Character Analysis #2

Name: _____

Date: _____

Title: _____

Author: _____

Character Impressions

- What kind of person is the main character? List words (adjectives) that describe your impressions of him or her.

- Then, for each of your impressions, write down a phrase from the story that supports it. Note the page number where you found this information.

My Impression of _____	Supporting Phrase	Page #

Character Analysis #3

Your Traits - My Traits

Character traits are those features that describe how someone **looks**, **feels**, **thinks**, and **acts**. For example, daring, resourceful, and clever are all character traits.

Compare one of the characters in your story to yourself.

In the outer circles, list character traits that are individual or unique to each of you. In the middle area, list the traits you have in common.

My unique character traits.

Our common character traits.

Unique character traits of _____

Character Analysis #4

Name: _____
Date: _____
Title: _____
Author: _____

Portrait Gallery

Draw a picture of **two** main characters and **two** minor characters from the novel.

Show the kind of person each character is by accurately depicting their usual facial expression.

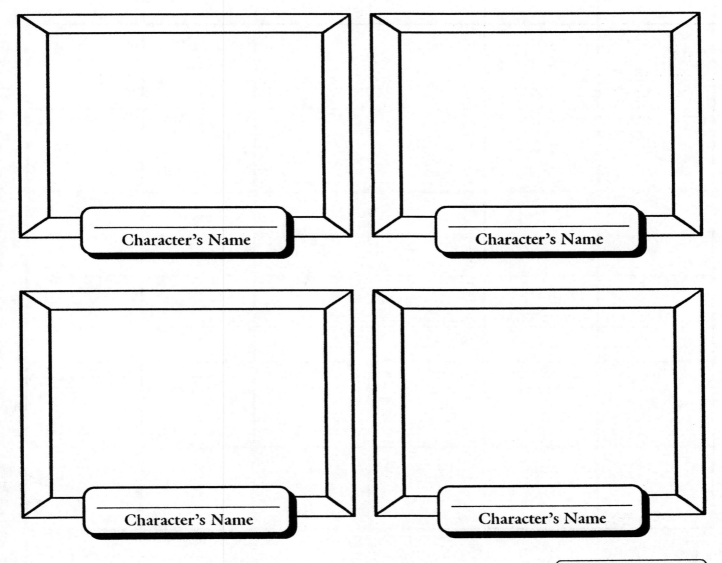

Character's Name

Character's Name

Character's Name

Character's Name

Character Analysis #5

Name: _____

Date: _____

Title: _____

Author: _____

Character Scrutiny

Choose **six** characters from the novel and complete the chart with appropriate words or phrases.

Character's Name	Description	Physical Appearance	Significance to the story	Relationship to the main character	Who does this character remind you of?

Character Analysis #6

Character Evaluation

Select a character from the book to **evaluate** by answering the questions below.

Character's Name

_____

What did the character do?

_____
_____
_____
_____
_____

Why did he or she do it?

_____
_____
_____
_____
_____

What do you like about this character?

_____
_____
_____
_____

How does this character react to others?

_____
_____
_____

What is the importance of this character to the book?

_____
_____
_____

What is unique about this character?

_____
_____
_____
_____

How does the character change in the story?

_____
_____
_____
_____

Which character from another novel does this character remind you of?

_____
_____
_____

Who do you know that is like this character? How are they similar?

_____
_____
_____

Character Analysis #7

Sketch Artist

Select a character from your novel. Use the author's description of the character to **draw** his or her portrait and fill in the sections below.

Character's name: _____

Physical description: _____

_____

Personality: _____

_____

Role in the story: _____

_____

Character Analysis #8

Feelings

Choose a character from your story.

In the table, **describe** how the character felt at the beginning, middle, and end of the story.

Give **examples** from the novel to show why he or she felt this way.

Record the page number where you found the example.

Character:_____

Feeling	Example from the beginning of the story	Page
Feeling	**Example from the middle of the story**	**Page**
Feeling	**Example from the end of the story**	**Page**

Character Analysis #9

Character Attribute Web

In each box, **record evidence** about a character using short phrases or words from the story.

His/Her Statements

_____
_____
_____
_____
_____
_____

His/Her Actions

_____
_____
_____
_____
_____
_____

His/Her Feelings

_____
_____
_____
_____
_____
_____

Character's Name
_____

His/Her Thoughts

_____
_____
_____
_____
_____
_____

How He/She Looks

_____
_____
_____
_____
_____
_____

Others' Actions Toward Him/Her

_____
_____
_____
_____
_____
_____

Character Analysis #10

Name: _____
Date: _____
Title: _____
Author: _____

Star Story Plotter

Summarize the plot of the story by completing the star plot organizer:

1. The story is about **Somebody**, or the main character.
2. This "Somebody" **Wants** something in the story.
3. **But**, there is a problem that interferes or prevents the Somebody from getting what he or she wants.
4. **So**, this character must find a way to solve the problem.
5. **Finally**, the story ends when...

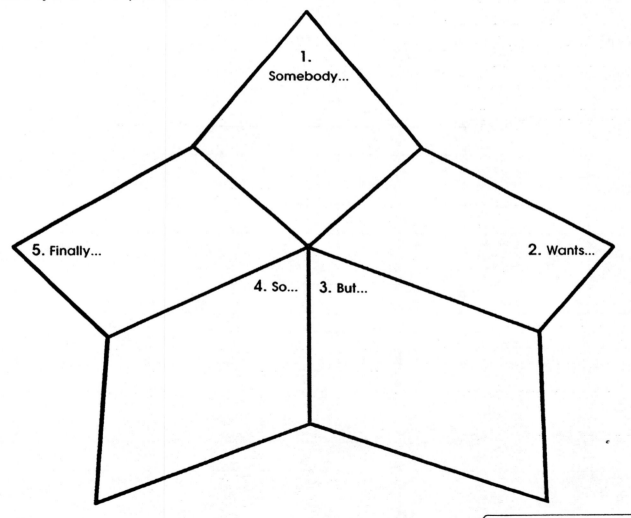

Summarizing Events #1

First, Then, Next

Retell the story by summarizing the story elements below.

The story takes places in _____ .

The story begins when _____
_____ .

The main characters are _____
_____ .

The main problem is _____
_____ .

First _____
_____ .

Then _____
_____ .

Next _____
_____ .

The story ends when _____
_____ .

Summarizing Events #2

Name: _____
Date: _____
Title: _____
Author: _____

Story Stones

Complete the outline summary of the story below. Then, use your outline to **rewrite** the story as a **picture book** in your own words. **Illustrate** each section and write it so a younger student could read it. When the pages are complete, add a cover with the title and staple it together into a book.

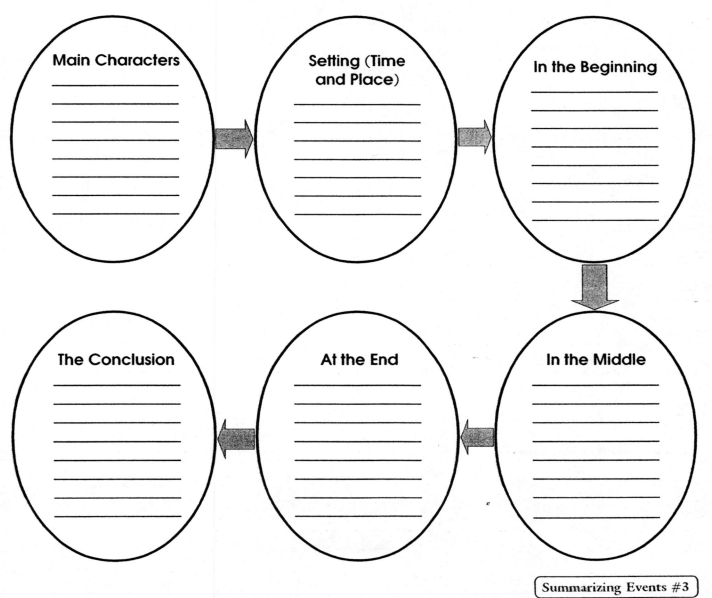

Main Characters

Setting (Time and Place)

In the Beginning

The Conclusion

At the End

In the Middle

Summarizing Events #3

Name: _____
Date: _____
Title: _____
Author: _____

Story Path

Summarize the events of the story using the organizer.

Make a sketch of the story's main idea in the center.

6. How did it happen?

_____
_____
_____

1. Who was in the story?

_____
_____
_____

5. Why did it occur?

_____
_____
_____

2. Where did it take place?

_____
_____
_____

4. What happened?

_____
_____
_____

3. When did it happen?

_____
_____

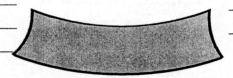

Summarizing Events #4

Name: _____
Date: _____
Title: _____
Author: _____

Story Steps

Follow the arrows to retell the events of the story in the order in which they happened.

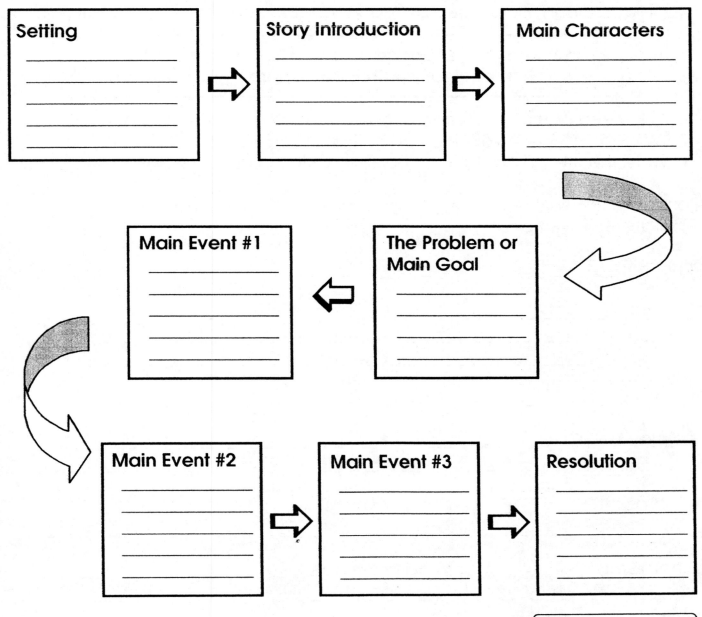

Setting
_____
_____
_____
_____

Story Introduction
_____
_____
_____
_____

Main Characters
_____
_____
_____
_____

Main Event #1
_____
_____
_____

The Problem or Main Goal
_____
_____
_____

Main Event #2
_____
_____
_____
_____

Main Event #3
_____
_____
_____
_____

Resolution
_____
_____
_____
_____

Summarizing Events #5

Name: _____
Date: _____
Title: _____
Author: _____

Playwright

Many plays are based on novels.

- **Turn your novel into a play** by using the sequential events of the story and adding details to them.
- Indicate which character says each line. Include character directions.

> **Example - Peter:** *(Appears on stage and whispers)* **Wendy, she's finally gotten out of here.**

- Add extra parts if you want to make the play more interesting.
- Write the name of your play at the top of your script.
- Write the title and author of your story at the end of the play.

Complete the outline to help you get started. Continue the script on separate sheets of paper.

Play Title: _____

Characters: _____   _____

               _____   _____

               _____   _____

Narrator: _____   _____

The play begins when _____

_____

(Character) _____ : (Stage directions) _____

_____

(Character) _____ : (Stage directions) _____

_____

Summarizing Events #6

Name: _____
Date: _____
Title: _____
Author: _____

Basic Book Report

Setting: (*Time and Place*) _____

Main Characters: _____

Overall Theme: (*What is the author's message about people in general?*)

_____

_____

Write a brief summary of the story. Be sure to put the events in sequence, in the order that they happened in the story. Include the problem, main events, and resolution.

_____

_____

_____

_____

_____

_____

What part of the story did you like the best? Explain your answer.

_____

_____

What part of the story did you like the least? Explain your answer.

_____

_____

Would you recommend this book to others? Why or why not?

_____

_____

Summarizing Events #7

Name: _____
Date: _____
Title: _____
Author: _____

Event Story Map

Fill in the **Setting**, **Characters**, **Problem**, and **Solution** in the first box. In the flow chart, record the **sequence of events** in the order in which they occur in the story.

Setting: Time: _____
              Place: _____
Characters: Main: _____
              Minor: _____
Problem: _____
_____
Solution: _____
_____

Summarizing Events #8

Nonfiction Retell Outline

Complete the outline to **summarize** the text.

What I thought I knew about this subject before reading the text: _____
_____
_____

After reading, I realized that _____
_____
_____

First I learned _____
_____
_____

Then I learned _____
_____
_____

Next I learned _____
_____
_____

Another interesting fact I learned was _____
_____
_____

I would like to learn more about _____
_____
_____

Summarizing Events #9

Name: _____

Date: _____

Title: _____

Author: _____

5W Story Map

Complete the 5W Map to summarize the novel.

Who is involved?
_____
_____
_____
_____
_____

Where and when does it happen?
_____
_____
_____
_____
_____

Why does it happen?
_____
_____
_____
_____
_____

What is the problem?
_____
_____
_____
_____
_____
_____

How is it solved?
_____
_____
_____
_____
_____
_____

Effect of the resolution?
_____
_____
_____
_____
_____
_____

Summarizing Events #10

Name: _____
Date: _____
Title: _____
Author: _____

Biography

A biography is a written account about someone's life. It presents real events from the life of the subject. The events the writer chooses to include usually provide some insight into the thoughts, feelings, development, or importance of the person being described, and the times in which he or she lived.

- **Choose** a character from your novel and write a one-page summary about the person's life.
- Find at least **five facts** about the character presented in the story. Include as much detail as you can to make your biography interesting.
- Avoid telling the reader what an incident means or says about the person. Instead, let the person's actions and words speak for themselves, and allow the reader to draw their own conclusions.

> **Example:** If you think Charles is a brave, courageous character, include details that portray him this way without saying that he is brave and courageous. You might write, "Charles fought the ferocious beast with his small sword."

Biography of _____

_____

_____

_____

_____

_____

_____

_____

_____

(Continue on the back.)

Add a New Character

Add a new character to your story. **List** some of his or her characteristics on the graphic organizer. Then, explain **why** this character would improve the story.

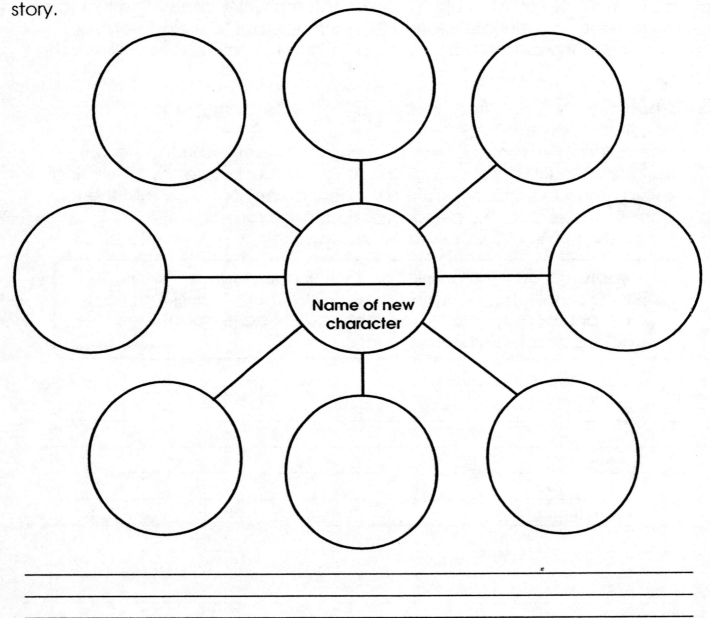

_____

_____

_____

Reasoning and Critical Thinking #2

Creative Designer

You have been hired as a creative designer to make a poster advertising the story you have read. Design a poster that reflects the story from your perspective. It should be interesting so that other people will want to read the story.

Brainstorm the things you found most appealing or interesting about the story. Select a focus for the poster from your list.

Interesting Facts:

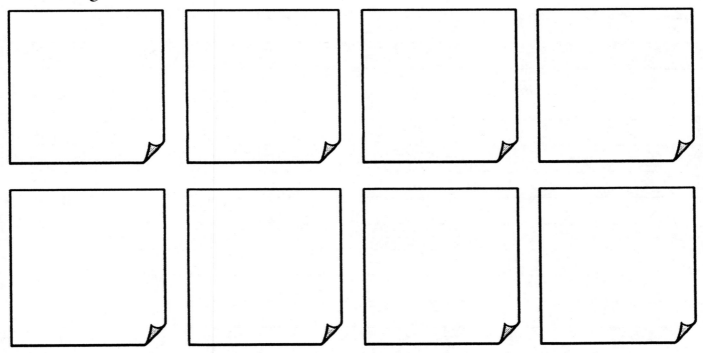

Materials you will need:

- a large piece of white construction paper or Bristol board
- markers, crayons, pencil crayons or paint
- a pencil

Reasoning and Critical Thinking #3

Name: _____

Date: _____

Title: _____

Author: _____

Join the Story

You move next door to the main character in your story.

Write a scene adding yourself to the story. **Describe** your new relationship:
Do you get along with _____? Are you friends?

How do you fit into the story? What do you do? Who do you do them with?
What is it like being the new kid?

_____

_____

_____

_____

_____

_____

_____

_____

_____

_____

_____

_____

_____

_____

_____

_____

_____

_____

_____

Reasoning and Critical Thinking #4

Name: _____

Date: _____

Title: _____

Author: _____

The Finale

The finale or ending of a story should leave the reader with a feeling of completion or satisfaction; the loose ends of the plot should be tied neatly together or resolved.

Are you satisfied with the way the novel ended? Did events unfold as you thought they would? Do you like how the author connected the details together?

Why or why not?

_____

_____

_____

Now write your own ending to the story. Remember to wrap up **all** the loose ends.

_____

_____

_____

_____

_____

_____

_____

_____

_____

_____

_____

_____

_____

Reasoning and Critical Thinking #5

Name: _____

Date: _____

Title: _____

Author: _____

Write a Letter

- Choose a character you liked in the story, and write a letter to him or her introducing yourself.
- Write about where you live, how old you are, and what your hobbies are.
- What would you like to know about him or her? Include this question in your letter.

_____
_____
_____

Date _____

Dear _____ ,

_____
_____
_____
_____
_____
_____
_____
_____
_____
_____

Yours truly,

_____

Text-to-Text Connections

- Compare two books that you have read.
- In the outside of the first circle, list the story elements of one book (setting, characters, plot, and resolution).
- In the outside of the second circle, list the story elements of the other book.
- In the middle section, list the similarities between the two books.

Story #1

Title _____

Author _____

Similarities between the stories.

Story #2

Title _____

Author _____

Reasoning and Critical Thinking #7

Name: _____
Date: _____
Title: _____
Author: _____

How Would You Solve It?

- List **five** problems that are encountered by characters in your story, in the first column.
- In the second column, note how the characters resolved each problem
- In the last column, describe how you might have solved the problems differently.

Problem	Characters' Solution	My Solution

Novel Conflict

Conflict in a story arises from the characters responding to a situation. The main character may be in conflict with 1) **another character**, 2) with **him or herself**, or 3) with some **outside force**, such as nature or society. (For example, a character may be struggling to survive during a blizzard.)

Write a **complete paragraph** that:

- Indentifies which of the three types of conflict occurs in your novel.
- Describes the **main conflict** and provides **supporting details** from the text.
- Explains the **events** that led up to the conflict, and how a **resolution** is achieved.

Include an opening statement, supporting details, and a conclusion that summarizes the information.

_____
_____
_____
_____
_____
_____
_____
_____
_____
_____
_____
_____
_____
_____

Name: _____
Date: _____
Title: _____
Author: _____

Cover Illustrator

- **Design** a new book cover for your novel. Make it unique!
- It should be colorful and interesting so that other people will want to read the book.
- Think about your favorite part of the story to get some ideas for the cover illustration.
- Write a **synopsis** of the story for the back cover. The synopsis is a brief overview of the story that describes what the story is about, and who the main characters are. The synopsis entices people to read the book by focusing on the conflict in the story.

Directions:

1. Fold a piece of construction paper in half. Then fold both ends of the paper under to make 2.5-centimeter (1-inch) flaps.

	Synopsis		Title Author Illustrator	
Fold here	_____ _____ _____ _____ _____			Fold here
Flap	Back Cover		Front Cover	Flap

2. Make an illustration on the front cover. Include the title, author, and illustrator above the picture.

3. Cut a piece of lined paper to fit on the back cover. On the paper, write a short synopsis of the story, and glue it to the back cover.

Name:	
Date:	
Title:	
Author:	

Is It Really a Noun?

A **noun** is a word that names a **person**, **place**, **thing**, or **idea**. A word's part of speech is determined by its *function* in a sentence, so a word that is a noun in one sentence, can be a **verb** or **adjective** in another.

For instance, the word **pet** is a noun when used in the sentence, *I want a pet*. In the sentence, *My pet hobby is sewing*, it is an adjective.

- Select **two** sentences from the text and write them below.
- Include the page number where you found each sentence.
- **Underline** the noun. On the next line, write why you think the word is a noun.
- Look up the word in a dictionary and verify whether or not it really is a noun.

Sentence #1: _____

_____

Page _____

I think this word is a noun because _____

_____

Dictionary verification: The underlined word is a noun. ☐ **Yes** ☐ **No**

Sentence #2: _____

_____

Page _____

I think this word is a noun because _____

_____

Dictionary verification: The underlined word is a noun. ☐ **Yes** ☐ **No**

Vocabulary Development #1

Abstract Nouns

Abstract nouns name **ideas**, **emotions**, and **feelings** rather than concrete things. Examples of abstract nouns are *quarrel*, *happiness*, *friendship*, *anger*, *beauty*, *sadness*, and *love*, to name a few. Write an abstract noun from your story in each circle below.

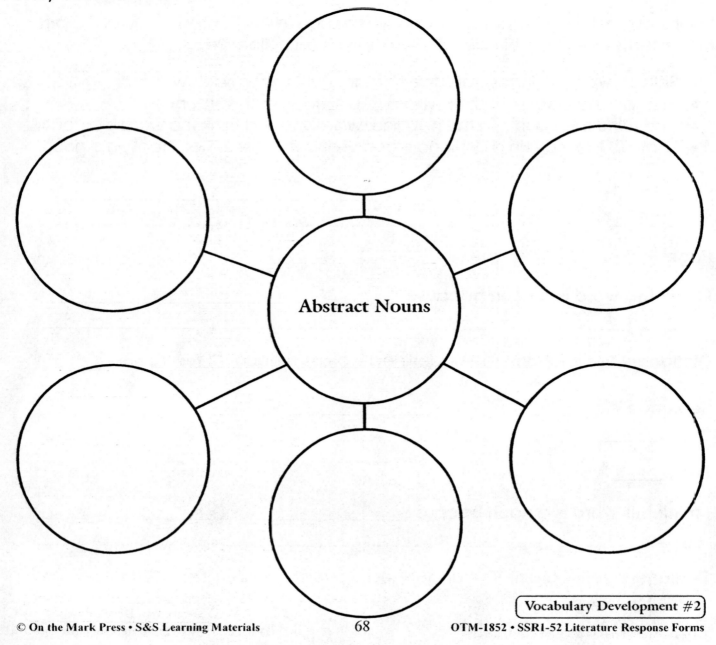

Abstract Nouns

Vocabulary Development #2

Name: _____

Date: _____

Title: _____

Author: _____

The Clothes Nouns Wear

An **adjective** is a word that tells us additional information about a noun. These words often appear before the nouns they modify, or after a linking verb. Adjectives are used to enhance the noun; they are like the *clothes* that nouns wear.

Find **four** adjectives in your story. On the first line below the adjective, write the noun it describes in the story. Then, list **three** other nouns it could also describe.

For example: HUGE
elephant
skyscraper
hippopotamus
appetite

1. _____

_____

_____

_____

_____

2. _____

_____

_____

_____

_____

3. _____

_____

_____

_____

_____

4. _____

_____

_____

_____

_____

Vocabulary Development #3

Name: _____

Date: _____

Title: _____

Author: _____

Vocabulary Expansion

Find **five** words in the story that you find interesting, confusing, or difficult to understand. Use a dictionary to complete the information below.

- Record the page number where you found the word.
- Write down the word, and put its pronunciation in brackets.
- Record two alternative meanings or synonyms, of the word.
- Note which part of speech the word functions as.
- Give an example of the word, using it in a new sentence.

Page __2__   **quest** (kwest)   **Synonyms:** search; pursuit
Part of Speech: noun
Example: Each year, the teams in the National Hockey League are involved in a *quest* to win the Stanley Cup.

Page _____   **Word** _____   **Pronunciation** (_____)
Part of Speech: _____   **Synonyms:** _____; _____
Example: _____

_____

Page _____   **Word** _____   **Pronunciation** (_____)
Part of Speech: _____   **Synonyms:** _____; _____
Example: _____

_____

Page _____   **Word** _____   **Pronunciation** (_____)
Part of Speech: _____   **Synonyms:** _____; _____
Example: _____

_____

Vocabulary Development #4

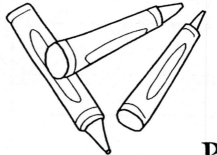

Name: _____
Date: _____
Title: _____
Author: _____

Picturing Adjectives

An **adjective** is a word that tells us additional information about a noun. These words often appear before the nouns they modify, or after a linking verb. Adjectives are used to enhance the meaning of a sentence; they are **describing words**.

Find **four** adjectives in your text. **Illustrate** the meaning of each one by drawing the word in such a way that it looks like its definition.

Example: It was a very chilly night.

chilly

Vocabulary Development #5

Get a Clue!

Using words and characters from your story, make a crossword puzzle for your classmates. Make at least **twelve clues** to solve in your puzzle. Black out boxes that are not used. Use the dictionary or thesaurus to help you with definitions and synonyms of words. Don't forget to make an answer sheet!

Example:

¹R	A	²T		
O		O		
²N	A	M	E	S
D				
³A	L	I	C	E

DOWN

1. Main character
2. Boy's name

ACROSS

1. Large rodent
2. "Ronda" and "Alice" are both _____
3. Ronda's friend

Across

1. _____
2. _____
3. _____
4. _____
5. _____
6. _____

Down

1. _____
2. _____
3. _____

4. _____
5. _____
6. _____

Vocabulary Development #6

Voracious Verbs

A **verb** is a "doing word" or a word that identifies an action. Verbs guide or direct the actions that nouns perform, or have performed on them.

To determine if a word is a verb, use it in another sentence to see if its form changes. If it is a verb, then the form will change (**example:** *I eat. He eats. I ate salmon yesterday.*)

List **ten verbs** from your story in the first column. In the second column, choose one verb that is tired or overused, and then find **six** other words that could be used instead.

> **Example: Tired Verb: *said***
>
> **Fresh verbs: *yelled, whispered, called, answered, replied, exclaimed***

1. _____
2. _____
3. _____
4. _____
5. _____
6. _____
7. _____
8. _____
9. _____
10. _____

Tired or overworked verb:

_____

Fresh or alternative verbs:

1. _____
2. _____
3. _____
4. _____
5. _____
6. _____

Vocabulary Development #7

Add-Ons

A **prefix** is a group of letters, or a syllable, added on to the **beginning** of another word that changes the word's meaning. For example, the prefix **dis-** added to the root word **appear** makes **disappear**.

Look in your story for words that begin with **dis-**, **en-**, **un-**, **re-**, and **in-** . Define what the prefix means from the context or the way the word is used in the story.

> **Example:** If <u>appear</u> means <u>to be seen</u>,
> **then** <u>disappear</u> means <u>it cannot be seen</u>.
> **So dis-** must mean **not**.

1. If _____ means _____ ,
   then _____ means _____ .
   So _____- must mean _____ .

2. If _____ means _____ ,
   then _____ means _____ .
   So _____- must mean _____ .

3. If _____ means _____ ,
   then _____ means _____ .
   So _____- must mean _____ .

Vocabulary Development #8

End-Its

A **suffix** is a group of letters, or syllable, added on to the **end** of a word to form another word. Often, adding a suffix can change the meaning of a word.

Look in your story for words that end in: **-ion, -ment, -est, -ant, -er, -ance, -less, -ful, -ness** and **-able**.

Define what the suffix means from the context or the way the word is used in the story.

> **Example:** If <u>home</u> means <u>a place one lives</u>,
> **then** <u>homeless</u> means <u>without a home</u>.
> **So -less** must mean **without**.

1. If _____ means _____ ,

   then _____ means _____ .

   So _____ - must mean _____ .

2. If _____ means _____ ,

   then _____ means _____ .

   So _____ - must mean _____ .

3. If _____ means _____ ,

   then _____ means _____ .

   So _____ - must mean _____ .

Vocabulary Development #9

Triangular Account

Look for **words** or **phrases** in the story that identify or describe the **key story elements** listed below.

Create a triangular account of the novel by completing each level of the triangle.

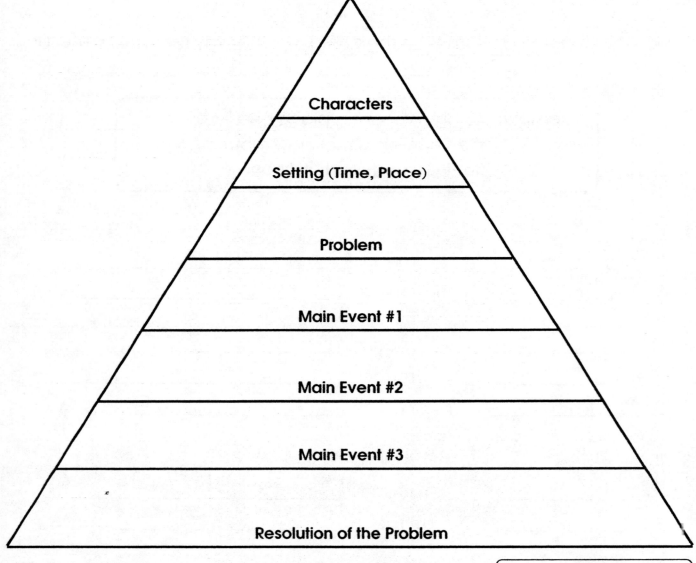

Characters

Setting (Time, Place)

Problem

Main Event #1

Main Event #2

Main Event #3

Resolution of the Problem

Vocabulary Development #10

Literature Response Forms

_____

_____

_____

_____

_____

_____

_____

_____

_____

_____

_____

_____

_____

_____

_____

_____

_____

_____

_____

_____

_____

_____

_____

_____

_____

Literature Response Forms

Literature
Response Forms

Literature
Response Forms

Literature
Response Forms

Literature
Response Forms

Publication Listing

Publication Listing

Code #	Title and Grade
SSN1-100	Indian in the Cupboard NS Gr. 4-6
SSPC-05	Insects B/W Pictures
SSPC-10	Inuit B/W Pictures
SSJ1-10	Inuit Community Gr. 3-4
SSN1-85	Ira Sleeps Over NS Gr. 1-3
SSN1-93	Iron Man NS Gr. 4-6
SSN1-193	Island of the Blue Dolphins NS 4-6
SSB1-11	It's a Dogs World Gr. 2-3
SSM1-05	It's a Marshmallow World Gr. 3
SSK1-05	It's About Time Gr. 2-4
SSC1-41	It's Christmas Time Gr. 3
SSH1-04	It's Circus Time Gr. 1
SSC1-43	It's Groundhog Day Gr. 3
SSB1-75	It's Maple Syrup Time Gr. 2-4
SSC1-40	It's Trick or Treat Time Gr. 2
SSN1-65	James & The Giant Peach NS 4-6
SSN1-106	Jane Eyre NS Gr. 7-8
SSPC-25	Japan B/W Pictures
SSA1-06	Japan Gr. 5-8
SSC1-05	Joy of Christmas Gr. 2
SSN1-161	Julie of the Wolves NS Gr. 7-8
SSB1-81	Jungles Gr. 2-3
SSE1-02	Junior Music for Fall Gr. 4-6
SSE1-05	Junior Music for Spring Gr. 4-6
SSE1-06	Junior Music for Winter Gr. 4-6
SSN1-151	Kate NS Gr. 4-6
SSN1-95	Kidnapped in the Yukon NS Gr. 4-6
SSN1-140	Kids at Bailey School Gr. 2-4
SSN1-176	King of the Wind NS Gr. 4-6
SSF1-29	Klondike Gold Rush Gr. 4-6
SSF1-33	Labour Movement in Canada Gr. 7-8
SSN1-152	Lamplighter NS Gr. 4-6
SSB1-98	Learning About Dinosaurs Gr. 3
SSN1-38	Learning About Giants Gr. 4-6
SSK1-22	Learning About Measurement Gr. 1-3
SSB1-46	Learning About Mice Gr. 3-5
SSK1-09	Learning About Money CDN Gr. 1-3
SSK1-19	Learning About Money USA Gr. 1-3
SSK1-23	Learning About Numbers Gr. 1-3
SSB1-69	Learning About Rocks & Soils Gr. 2-3
SSK1-08	Learning About Shapes Gr. 1-3
SSB1-100	Learning About Simple Machines 1-3
SSK1-04	Learning About the Calendar Gr. 2-3
SSK1-10	Learning About Time Gr. 1-3
SSH1-17	Learning About Transportation Gr. 1
SSB1-02	Leaves Gr. 2-3
SSN1-50	Legends Gr. 4-6
SSC1-27	Lest We Forget Gr. 4-6
SSJ1-13	Let's Look at Canada Gr. 4-6
SSJ1-16	Let's Visit Alberta Gr. 2-4
SSJ1-15	Let's Visit British Columbia Gr. 2-4
SSJ1-03	Let's Visit Canada Gr. 3
SSJ1-18	Let's Visit Manitoba Gr. 2-4
SSJ1-21	Let's Visit New Brunswick Gr. 2-4
SSJ1-27	Let's Visit NFLD & Labrador Gr. 2-4
SSJ1-30	Let's Visit North West Terr. Gr. 2-4
SSJ1-20	Let's Visit Nova Scotia Gr. 2-4
SSJ1-34	Let's Visit Nunavut Gr. 2-4
SSJ1-17	Let's Visit Ontario Gr. 2-4
SSQ1-08	Let's Visit Ottawa Big Book Pkg 1-3
SSJ1-19	Let's Visit PEI Gr. 2-4
SSJ1-31	Let's Visit Québec Gr. 2-4
SSJ1-14	Let's Visit Saskatchewan Gr. 2-4
SSJ1-28	Let's Visit Yukon Gr. 2-4
SSN1-130	Life & Adv. of Santa Claus NS 7-8
SSB1-10	Life in a Pond Gr. 3-4
SSF1-30	Life in the Middle Ages Gr. 7-8
SSB1-103	Light & Sound Gr. 4-6
SSN1-219	Light in the Forest NS Gr. 7-8
SSN1-121	Light on Hogback Hill NS Gr. 4-6
SSN1-46	Lion, Witch & the Wardrobe NS 4-6
SSR1-51	Literature Response Forms Gr. 1-3
SSR1-52	Literature Response Forms Gr. 4-6
SSN1-28	Little House Big Woods NS 4-6
SSN1-233	Little House on the Prairie NS 4-6
SSN1-111	Little Women NS Gr. 7-8
SSN1-115	Live from the Fifth Grade NS 4-6
SSN1-141	Look Through My Window NS 4-6
SSN1-112	Look! Visual Discrimination Gr. P-1
SSN1-61	Lost & Found NS Gr. 4-6
SSN1-109	Lost in the Barrens NS Gr. 7-8
SSJ1-08	Lumbering Community Gr. 3-4
SSN1-167	Magic School Bus Gr. 1-3
SSN1-247	Magic Treehouse Gr. 1-3
SSB1-78	Magnets Gr. 3-5
SSD1-03	Making Sense of Our Senses K-1
SSN1-146	Mama's Going to Buy You a NS 4-6
SSB1-94	Mammals Gr. 1
SSB1-95	Mammals Gr. 2
SSB1-96	Mammals Gr. 3
SSB1-97	Mammals Gr. 5-6
SSN1-160	Maniac Magee NS Gr. 4-6
SSA1-19	Mapping Activities & Outlines! 4-8
SSA1-17	Mapping Skills Gr. 1-3
SSA1-07	Mapping Skills Gr. 4-6
SST1-10A	March Gr. JK/SK
SST1-10B	March Gr. 1
SST1-10C	March Gr. 2-3
SSB1-57	Marvellous Marsupials Gr. 4-6
SSK1-01	Math Signs & Symbols Gr. 1-3
SSB1-116	Matter & Materials Gr. 1-3
SSB1-117	Matter & Materials Gr. 4-6
SSH1-03	Me, I'm Special! Gr. P-1
SSK1-16	Measurement Gr. 4-8
SSC1-02	Medieval Christmas Gr. 4-6
SSPC-09	Medieval Life B/W Pictures
SSC1-07	Merry Christmas Gr. P-K
SSK1-15	Metric Measurement Gr. 4-8
SSN1-13	Mice in Literature Gr. 3-5
SSB1-70	Microscopy Gr. 4-6
SSN1-180	Midnight Fox NS Gr. 4-6
SSN1-243	Midwife's Apprentice NS Gr. 4-6
SSJ1-07	Mining Community Gr. 3-4
SSK1-17	Money Talks – Cdn Gr. 3-6
SSK1-18	Money Talks – USA Gr. 3-6
SSB1-56	Monkeys & Apes Gr. 4-6
SSN1-43	Monkeys in Literature Gr. 2-4
SSN1-54	Monster Mania Gr. 4-6
SSN1-97	Mouse & the Motorcycle NS 4-6
SSN1-94	Mr. Poppers Penguins NS Gr. 4-6
SSN1-201	Mrs. Frisby & Rats NS Gr. 4-6
SSR1-13	Milti-Level Spelling Program Gr. 3-6
SSR1-26	Multi-Level Spelling USA Gr. 3-6
SSK1-31	Addition & Subtraction Drills 1-3
SSK1-32	Multiplication & Division Drills 4-6
SSK1-30	Multiplication Drills Gr. 4-6
SSA1-14	My Country! The USA! Gr. 2-4
SSN1-186	My Side of the Mountain NS 7-8
SSN1-58	Mysteries, Monsters & Magic Gr. 6-8
SSN1-37	Mystery at Blackrock Island NS 7-8
SSN1-80	Mystery House NS 4-6
SSN1-157	Nate the Great & Sticky Case NS 1-3
SSF1-23	Native People of North America 4-6
SSF1-25	New France Part 1 Gr. 7-8
SSF1-27	New France Part 2 Gr. 7-8
SSA1-10	New Zealand Gr. 4-8
SSN1-51	Newspapers Gr. 5-8
SSN1-47	No Word for Goodbye NS Gr. 7-8
SSPC-03	North American Animals B/W Pictures
SSF1-22	North American Natives Gr. 2-4
SSN1-75	Novel Ideas Gr. 4-6
SST1-06A	November JK/SK
SST1-06B	November Gr. 1
SST1-06C	November Gr. 2-3
SSN1-244	Number the Stars NS Gr. 4-6
SSY1-03	Numeration Gr. 1-3
SSPC-14	Nursery Rhymes B/W Pictures
SSN1-12	Nursery Rhymes Gr. P-1
SSN1-59	On the Banks of Plum Creek NS 4-6
SSN1-220	One in Middle Green Kangaroo NS 1-3
SSN1-145	One to Grow On NS Gr. 4-6
SSB1-27	Opossums Gr. 3-5
SSJ1-23	Ottawa Gr. 7-9
SSJ1-39	Our Canadian Governments Gr. 5-8
SSF1-14	Our Global Heritage Gr. 4-6
SSH1-12	Our Neighbourhoods Gr. 4-6
SSB1-72	Our Trash Gr. 2-3
SSB1-51	Our Universe Gr. 5-8
SSB1-86	Outer Space Gr. 1-2
SSA1-18	Outline Maps of the World Gr. 1-8
SSB1-67	Owls Gr. 4-6
SSN1-31	Owls in the Family NS Gr. 4-6
SSL1-02	Oxbridge Owl & The Library Gr. 4-6
SSB1-71	Pandas, Polar & Penguins Gr. 4-6
SSN1-52	Paperbag Princess NS Gr. 1-3
SSR1-11	Passion of Jesus: A Play Gr. 7-8
SSA1-12	Passport to Adventure Gr. 4-5
SSR1-06	Passport to Adventure Gr. 7-8
SSR1-04	Personal Spelling Dictionary Gr. 2-5
SSPC-29	Pets B/W Pictures
SSE1-03	Phantom of the Opera Gr. 7-9
SSN1-171	Phoebe Gilman Author Study Gr. 2-3
SSY1-06	Phonics Gr. 1-3
SSN1-237	Pierre Berton Author Study Gr. 7-8
SSN1-179	Pigman NS Gr. 7-8
SSN1-48	Pigs in Literature Gr. 2-4
SSN1-99	Pinballs NS Gr. 4-6
SSN1-60	Pippi Longstocking NS Gr. 4-6
SSF1-12	Pirates Gr. 4-6
SSK1-13	Place Value Gr. 4-6
SSB1-77	Planets Gr. 3-6
SSR1-74	Poetry Prompts Gr. 1-3
SSR1-75	Poetry Prompts Gr. 4-6
SSB1-66	Popcorn Fun Gr. 2-3
SSB1-20	Porcupines Gr. 3-5
SSR1-55	Practice Manuscript Gr. Pk-2
SSR1-56	Practice Cursive Gr. 2-4
SSF1-24	Prehistoric Times Gr. 4-6
SSE1-01	Primary Music for Fall Gr. 1-3
SSE1-04	Primary Music for Spring Gr. 1-3
SSE1-07	Primary Music for Winter Gr. 1-3
SSJ1-47	Prime Ministers of Canada Gr. 4-8
SSK1-20	Probability & Inheritance Gr. 7-10
SSN1-49	Question of Loyalty NS Gr. 7-8
SSN1-26	Rabbits in Literature Gr. 2-4
SSB1-17	Raccoons Gr. 3-5
SSN1-207	Radio Fifth Grade NS Gr. 4-6
SSB1-52	Rainbow of Colours Gr. 4-6
SSN1-144	Ramona Quimby Age 8 NS 4-6
SSJ1-09	Ranching Community Gr. 3-4
SSY1-08	Reading for Meaning Gr. 1-3
SSN1-165	Reading Response Forms Gr. 1-3
SSN1-239	Reading Response Forms Gr. 4-6
SSN1-234	Reading with Arthur Gr. 1-3
SSN1-249	Reading with Canadian Authors 1-3
SSN1-200	Reading with Curious George Gr. 2-4
SSN1-230	Reading with Eric Carle Gr. 1-3
SSN1-251	Reading with Kenneth Oppel Gr. 4-6
SSN1-127	Reading with Mercer Mayer Gr. 1-2
SSN1-07	Reading with Motley Crew Gr. 2-3
SSN1-142	Reading with Robert Munsch 1-3
SSN1-06	Reading with the Super Sleuths 4-6
SSN1-08	Reading with the Ziggles Gr. 1
SST1-11A	Red Gr. JK/SK
SSN1-147	Refuge NS Gr. 7-8
SSC1-44	Remembrance Day Gr. 1-3
SSPC-23	Reptiles B/W Pictures
SSB1-42	Reptiles Gr. 4-6
SSN1-110	Return of the Indian NS Gr. 4-6
SSN1-225	River NS Gr. 7-8
SSE1-08	Robert Schuman, Composer Gr. 6-9
SSN1-83	Robot Alert NS Gr. 4-6
SSB1-65	Rocks & Minerals Gr. 4-6
SSN1-149	Romeo & Juliet NS Gr. 7-8
SSB1-88	Romping Reindeer Gr. K-3
SSN1-21	Rumplestiltskin NS Gr. 1-3
SSN1-153	Runaway Ralph NS Gr. 4-6
SSN1-103	Sadako & 1000 Paper Cranes NS 4-6
SSD1-04	Safety Gr. 2-4
SSN1-42	Sarah Plain & Tall NS Gr. 4-6
SSC1-34	School in September Gr. 4-6
SSPC-01	Sea Creatures B/W Pictures
SSB1-79	Sea Creatures Gr. 1-3
SSN1-64	Secret Garden NS Gr. 4-6
SSB1-90	Seeds & Weeds Gr. 2-3
SSY1-02	Sentence Writing Gr. 1-3
SST1-07A	September JK/SK
SST1-07B	September Gr. 1
SST1-07C	September Gr. 2-3
SSN1-30	Serendipity Series Gr. 3-5
SSC1-22	Shamrocks on Parade Gr. 1
SSC1-24	Shamrocks, Harps & Shillelaghs 3-4
SSR1-66	Shakespeare Shorts-Perf Arts Gr. 1-4
SSR1-67	Shakespeare Shorts-Perf Arts Gr. 4-6
SSR1-68	Shakespeare Shorts-Lang Arts Gr. 2-4
SSR1-69	Shakespeare Shorts-Lang Arts Gr. 4-6
SSB1-74	Sharks Gr. 4-6
SSN1-158	Shiloh NS Gr. 4-6
SSN1-84	Sideways Stories Wayside NS 4-6
SSN1-181	Sight Words Activities Gr. 1
SSB1-99	Simple Machines Gr. 4-6
SSN1-19	Sixth Grade Secrets 4-6
SSG1-04	Skill Building with Slates Gr. K-8
SSN1-118	Skinny Bones NS Gr. 4-6
SSB1-24	Skunks Gr. 3-5
SSN1-191	Sky is Falling NS Gr. 4-6
SSB1-83	Slugs & Snails Gr. 1-3
SSB1-55	Snakes Gr. 4-6
SST1-12A	Snow Gr. JK/SK
SST1-12B	Snow Gr. 1
SST1-12C	Snow Gr. 2-3
SSB1-76	Solar System Gr. 4-6
SSPC-44	South America B/W Pictures
SSA1-11	South America Gr. 4-6
SSB1-05	Space Gr. 2-3
SSR1-34	Spelling Blacklines Gr. 1
SSR1-35	Spelling Blacklines Gr. 2
SSR1-14	Spelling Gr. 1
SSR1-15	Spelling Gr. 2
SSR1-16	Spelling Gr. 3
SSR1-17	Spelling Gr. 4
SSR1-18	Spelling Gr. 5
SSR1-19	Spelling Gr. 6
SSR1-27	Spelling Worksavers #1 Gr. 3-5
SSM1-02	Spring Celebration Gr. 2-3
SST1-01A	Spring Gr. JK/SK
SST1-01B	Spring Gr. 1
SST1-01C	Spring Gr. 2-3
SSM1-01	Spring in the Garden Gr. 1-2
SSB1-26	Squirrels Gr. 3-5
SSB1-112	Stable Structures & Mechanisms 3
SSG1-05	Steps in the Research Process 5-8
SSG1-02	Stock Market Gr. 7-8
SSN1-139	Stone Fox NS Gr. 4-6
SSN1-214	Stone Orchard NS Gr. 7-8
SSN1-01	Story Book Land of Witches Gr. 2-3
SSR1-64	Story Starters Gr. 1-3
SSR1-65	Story Starters Gr. 4-6
SSR1-73	Story Starters Gr. 1-6
SSY1-09	Story Writing Gr. 1-3
SSB1-111	Structures, Mechanisms & Motion 2
SSN1-211	Stuart Little NS Gr. 4-6
SSK1-29	Subtraction Drills Gr. 1-3
SSY1-05	Subtraction Gr. 1-3
SSY1-11	Successful Language Pract. Gr. 1-3
SSY1-12	Successful Math Practice Gr. 1-3
SSW1-09	Summer Learning Gr. K-1
SSW1-10	Summer Learning Gr. 1-2
SSW1-11	Summer Learning Gr. 2-3
SSW1-12	Summer Learning Gr. 3-4
SSW1-13	Summer Learning Gr. 4-5
SSW1-14	Summer Learning Gr. 5-6
SSN1-159	Summer of the Swans NS Gr. 4-6
SSZ1-02	Summer Olympics Gr. 4-6
SSM1-07	Super Summer Gr. 1-2
SSN1-18	Superfudge NS Gr. 4-6
SSA1-08	Switzerland Gr. 4-6
SSN1-20	T.V. Kid NS. Gr. 4-6
SSA1-15	Take a Trip to Australia Gr. 2-3
SSB1-102	Taking Off With Flight Gr. 1-3
SSN1-259	Tale of Despereaux Gr. 4-6
SSN1-55	Tales of the Fourth Grade NS 4-6
SSN1-188	Taste of Blackberries NS Gr. 4-6
SSK1-07	Teaching Math Through Sports 6-9
SST1-09A	Thanksgiving JK/SK
SST1-09C	Thanksgiving Gr. 2-3
SSN1-77	There's a Boy in the Girls.. NS 4-6
SSN1-143	This Can't Be Happening NS Gr. 4-6
SSN1-05	Three Billy Goats Gruff NS Gr. 1-3
SSN1-72	Ticket to Curlew NS Gr. 4-6
SSN1-82	Timothy of the Cay NS Gr. 7-8
SSF1-32	Titanic Gr. 4-6
SSN1-222	To Kill a Mockingbird NS Gr. 7-8
SSN1-195	Toilet Paper Tigers NS Gr. 4-6
SSJ1-35	Toronto Gr. 4-8
SSH1-02	Toy Shelf Gr. P-K
SSPC-24	Toys B/W Pictures
SSN1-163	Traditional Poetry Gr. 7-10
SSH1-13	Transportation Gr. 4-6
SSW1-01	Transportation Snip Art
SSB1-03	Trees Gr. 2-3
SSA1-01	Tropical Rainforest Gr. 4-6
SSN1-56	Trumpet of the Swan NS Gr. 4-6
SSN1-81	Tuck Everlasting NS Gr. 4-6
SSN1-126	Turtles in Literature Gr. 1-3
SSN1-45	Underground to Canada NS 4-6
SSN1-27	Unicorns in Literature Gr. 3-5
SSJ1-44	Upper & Lower Canada Gr. 7-8
SSN1-192	Using Novels Canadian North Gr. 7-8
SSC1-14	Valentines Day Gr. 5-8
SSPC-45	Vegetables B/W Pictures
SSY1-01	Very Hungry Caterpillar NS 30/Pkg 1-3
SSF1-13	Victorian Era Gr. 7-8
SSC1-35	Victorian Christmas Gr. 5-8
SSF1-17	Viking Age Gr. 4-6
SSN1-206	War with Grandpa SN Gr. 4-6
SSB1-91	Water Gr. 2-4
SSN1-166	Watership Down NS Gr. 7-8
SSH1-16	Ways We Travel Gr. P-K
SSN1-101	Wayside Sch. Little Stranger NS 4-6
SSN1-76	Wayside Sch. Is Falling Down NS 4-6
SSB1-60	Weather Gr. 4-6
SSN1-17	Wee Folk in Literature Gr. 3-5
SSPC-08	Weeds B/W Pictures
SSQ1-04	Welcome Back – Big Book Pkg 1-3
SSB1-73	Whale Preservation Gr. 5-8
SSH1-08	What is a Community? Gr. 2-4
SSH1-01	What is a Family? Gr. 2-3
SSH1-09	What is a School? Gr. 1-2
SSJ1-32	What is Canada? Gr. P-K
SSN1-79	What is RAD? Read & Discover 2-4
SSB1-62	What is the Weather Today? Gr. 2-4
SSN1-194	What's a Daring Detective NS 4-6
SSH1-10	What's My Number Gr. P-K
SSR1-02	What's the Scoop on Words Gr. 4-6
SSN1-73	Where the Red Fern Grows NS 7-8
SSN1-87	Where the Wild Things Are NS 1-3

Publication Listing

Code #	Title and Grade	Code #	Title and Grade	Code #	Title and Grade	Code #	Title and Grade
SSN1-187	Whipping Boy NS Gr. 4-6						
SSN1-226	Who is Frances Rain? NS Gr. 4-6						
SSN1-74	Who's Got Gertie & How...? NS 4-6						
SSN1-131	Why did the Underwear ... NS 4-6						
SSC1-28	Why Wear a Poppy? Gr. 2-3						
SSJ1-11	Wild Animals of Canada Gr. 2-3						
SSPC-07	Wild Flowers B/W Pictures						
SSB1-18	Winter Birds Gr. 2-3						
SSZ1-03	Winter Olympics Gr. 4-6						
SSM1-04	Winter Wonderland Gr. 1						
SSC1-01	Witches Gr. 3-4						
SSN1-213	Wolf Island NS Gr. 1-3						
SSE1-09	Wolfgang Amadeus Mozart 6-9						
SSB1-23	Wolves Gr. 3-5						
SSC1-20	Wonders of Easter Gr. 2						
SSB1-35	World of Horses Gr. 4-6						
SSB1-13	World of Pets Gr. 2-3						
SSF1-26	World War II Gr. 7-8						
SSN1-221	Wrinkle in Time NS Gr. 7-8						
SSPC-02	Zoo Animals B/W Pictures						
SSB1-08	Zoo Animals Gr. 1-2						
SSB1-09	Zoo Celebration Gr. 3-4						